David Clilverd.

Salmon Fisheries
of
Scotland

Salmon Fisheries
of
Scotland

**Association of Scottish District
Salmon Fishery Boards**

Published by

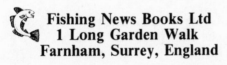 **Fishing News Books Ltd
1 Long Garden Walk
Farnham, Surrey, England**

ISBN 0 85238 091 7

Printed in Great Britain by
The Press at Coombelands Limited
Coombelands, Addlestone, Surrey KT15 1JN

Foreword

by the Rt Hon Viscount Thurso of Ulbster, JP,

President of the Association of Scottish
District Salmon Fishery Boards.

'The Salmon is accounted the King of fresh-water fish . . . . .' wrote Izaac Walton in 1653 and then went on to describe the life history of this fascinating creature. Today the Salmon occupies the same pinnacle of importance, especially in Scotland, as he did in Walton's time, yet over three hundred years later much of his life cycle is still shrouded in mystery. Nevertheless, great strides in our knowledge of how to manage salmon fisheries have been made and a complex legal and administrative structure has been built up to guard and guide our salmon fishing industry.

Scottish salmon fisheries employ many hundreds of people directly and an even greater number indirectly, often in remote rural areas where other work is hard to find. They provide food; they offer recreation; they give employment and they earn substantial amounts of foreign currency. This considerable contribution to Scotland's economy is being made at a time when the salmon fisheries of other countries have been in decline and yet the fisheries of Scotland have increased both their catch and their value. In an age of increasing pollution and growing demands on water supplies, this feat must be regarded as an outstanding conservation success story.

But we must not be complacent. There is room yet for improvement and there is need always for vigilance. We must adjust, too, to changes in a changing world. So it is important that those who are interested in salmon and those who are charged with the responsibility of managing salmon fisheries should have a good understanding of their present organisation and administration. With this in mind, this booklet has been prepared by the Association of Scottish District Salmon Fishery Boards in consultation with the Freshwater Fisheries Laboratory of the Department of Agriculture and Fisheries for Scotland.

It is intended to be a brief guide for all those interested in Scottish salmon fisheries. It does not attempt to deal in depth with any part of this complicated and fascinating subject but instead gives references for further reading for the use of those who would like greater detail about any particular aspect of it. What it does try to do is to promote understanding of the legal and administrative framework within which we are trying at the same time to conserve and to utilize our salmon fishing heritage, in the hope that the knowledge so passed on will help to ensure the future prosperity of the Scottish salmon fishing industry for the generations which will follow us.

Thurso.

Acknowledgements

The task of preparing this booklet was undertaken by a sub-committee of the Council of the Association of Scottish District Salmon Fishery Boards. The members of the sub-committee were:—

Mr N W Graesser
Mr J R W Stansfeld
Mr N R Beattie
Mr J M Thomson
Mr N A Cockburn

The Council wish to thank the sub-committee for bringing this project to a successful conclusion. It is particularly indebted to Mr. J R W Stansfeld, who undertook the onerous role of Editor. Grateful acknowledgements are also due to the following:—

Mr A V Holden, Officer-in-Charge of the Freshwater Fisheries Laboratory at Faskally, and his colleague, Mr W R Munro, who attended the meetings of the sub-committee and provided valuable material and advice on various technical subjects.

Mr B B Parrish, Director of Fisheries Research for Scotland, and Mr S D Sedgwick, Inspector of Salmon Fisheries for Scotland, both of whom read the booklet in draft form and contributed helpful criticisms and suggestions.

Mrs M Gammie, Illustrator at the Marine Laboratory, Aberdeen, who drew the excellent illustrations of the legal methods of netting salmon in Scotland.

The North of Scotland Hydro Electric Board, who made available the salmon count figures on their various schemes, and revised the section dealing with hydro electric development.

The booklet is, for the most part, a record of facts: any inferences and opinions which it may contain are those of the Association alone.

Association of Scottish District
Salmon Fishery Boards,
19 Ainslie Place,
Edinburgh, EH3 6AY.

Contents

Illustrations

1 Salmon

The 'salmon' is defined in the *Salmon and Freshwater Fisheries (Protection) (Scotland) Act 1951* as including 'all migratory fish of the species *Salmo salar* and *Salmo trutta* and commonly known as salmon and sea trout respectively'.

The Atlantic salmon, *Salmo salar,* is the only native salmon of the North Atlantic and is distributed on the western side, from Ungava Bay to the Connecticut River, and on the eastern side, from Portugal to the Arctic coast of Russia and in the Baltic.

The Atlantic salmon is anadromous, meaning that it returns to spawn in fresh water after making most of its growth in the sea. Most salmon return to the rivers from which they migrated as juveniles. Fish which return to spawn after only one winter in the sea are called grilse, and those which spend two or three winters in the sea, and occasionally more, are referred to as salmon. Although salmon may enter the rivers at any time of year, there are early runs of spring salmon in some rivers. However, in most rivers the main runs of salmon are in the summer and early autumn, and the grilse run occurs generally during a period from June to August.

Spawning occurs from October to January, in the reaches of the river where suitable clean gravel exists. The female deposits her eggs (ova) in the gravel, where they are simultaneously fertilized by the male. The ova hatch, in late March or early April, into alevins with a yolk sac attached, sustaining the young fish in the gravel for four or five weeks. When the yolk sac is absorbed, the small salmon (fry) emerge from the gravel and feed on aquatic organisms.

At the end of their first year of life they are known as parr, and they may remain in this stage until the spring of their second, third or even fourth year before turning silver and becoming smolts. These smolts descend to the sea during March to June, and migrate to feeding grounds which are not fully known, but which may be as far away as Greenland if they spend two or more years at sea.

After spawning, those spent fish (kelts) which survive, return to the sea. Mortality after spawning is high, especially among the males, but those kelts which reach the sea may feed and ripen to spawn again, although salmon rarely spawn more than twice. Some female fish fail to spawn, and these ('baggots' or 'rawners') are sometimes caught during the spring full of unshed ova.

The sea trout has a similar life history to that of the salmon, but does not carry out such extensive sea migrations as salmon, nor move so far from the coast. Unlike the salmon, some sea trout return to freshwater in the late summer or autumn of the year in which they migrated as smolts, and are then known as finnock, whitling or herling. A small proportion of finnock spawn. Sea trout may survive to spawn several times and there are records of fish which have spawned up to twelve times.

There are large populations of salmon of several species in the Pacific Ocean, but these belong to a distinct and separate genus (*Oncorhynchus*) and should not be confused with *Salmo salar* indigenous to the Atlantic.

FURTHER READING

Calderwood, W L	1907	*The Life of the Salmon* (Arnold)
Malloch, P D	1910	*Life History and Habits of the Salmon, Sea Trout, Trout, Etc.* (A & C Black)
Menzies, W J M	1925	*The Salmon* (Blackwood)
Nall, G H	1930	*Life History of the Sea Trout* (Seely Service)
Jones, J W	1959	*The Salmon* (Collins)
Frost, W E and Brown, M E	1967	*The Trout* (Collins)
Scott, J	1969	*Seatrout Fishing* (Lonsdale Library)
Mills, D H	1971	*Salmon and Trout* (Oliver & Boyd)

2 The History and Distribution of Salmon Fisheries in Scotland

(a) History

The salmon fisheries of Scotland have been the subject of legislation since 1318. They have always been an important resource to the people of Scotland, but detailed records of catches have been compiled only since 1952. Records before that date are not complete and give only an indication of general trends. It does not appear that there has been any marked change in the total Scottish salmon catch over the last 50 years. However, long term cycles are indicated by the figures that exist and these show peaks in the 1880s and 1960s with low points in the 1850s and the 1940s. On the other hand there have been marked changes in the distribution of different runs within the total catch, with grilse runs being predominant during the high points of the cycle. Appendix V gives important statistics relating to salmon fisheries in recent years.

(b) Distribution

The geography of Scotland places the watershed between east and west coasts comparatively close to the west coast. Accordingly the east coast rivers are fewer in number and much larger than those on the west. The more valuable salmon fishings are, therefore, on the east coast, where salmon are more numerous and run over a longer period. On the whole the west coast rivers are shorter and support grilse and sea trout. Appendix IV gives the comparative catches in the main areas of Scotland and the map opposite page 17 shows the rivers.

FURTHER READING

Report of Salmon Commission 1825.
Report of Salmon Commission (Scotland) 1836.
Report of Salmon Commission (Scotland) 1860.
Report of Salmon Commission (Scotland) 1871.
Report of Salmon Commission 1902.

3 Ownership of Salmon Fishings

(a) Separate Heritable Estate

All rights of salmon fishing in Scotland—whether in the sea, in estuaries or in rivers—belonged originally to the Crown. From a very early period, however, these rights were in many cases conveyed to individuals by means of written Crown grants. All private titles to salmon fishing are derived from such grants and must be based on deeds recorded in the Register of Sasines, kept at Meadowbank House, Edinburgh. In certain cases, however, the unchallenged possession of salmon fisheries for the appropriate prescriptive period may be relevant in establishing a right to such fisheries. The right to fish for salmon is not dependent on the ownership of adjoining land, but is a separate heritable estate which can be bought, sold or leased. Salmon fishings in Orkney and Shetland are an exceptional case, and different rules apply. (See Chapter 5).

(b) Crown's Interest

The grants by the Crown of salmon fishings in the sea are not so numerous as those of fishings in rivers. Although some grants have been made of fishings in the sea, the right to fish for salmon around the greater part of the Scottish coast still belongs to the Crown. This right is administered by the Crown Estate Commissioners at 10, Charlotte

Square, Edinburgh. It is the general practice of the Crown to lease their salmon fishings to tacksmen, or lessees, for periods of nine years. The fishings are advertised quite widely and tacksmen submit their offers in writing to the Crown. There is no security of tenure at the end of the lease. Certain river fishings are also leased by the Crown.

(c) Valuation Roll

The Assessor of each local authority region prepares and publishes annually a Valuation Roll which lists the description and situation of all rateable property in his area. The Roll is an important document as it contains the names and addresses of proprietors, tenants, occupiers and also the annual value. Salmon rod fishings are rateable and, therefore, should appear in the Roll if they are of any value. Salmon net fishings also appear in areas where there is a District Salmon Fishery Board, for the purposes of assessment. (See Chapter 7).

(d) Tracing Ownership

The ownership of particular salmon fishings is generally well known locally. When in difficulty, however, information on ownership may be obtained from the Crown Estate Commissioners, the Regional Assessor or the Clerk to the District Salmon Fishery Board.

(e) Owner and Lessee

Salmon fishings are often leased. A lease of salmon fishings for more than one year must be in writing. Rod and net fishings in the same water may be let to different lessees. The right of fishing by either method may be reserved wholly or partly by the owner.

(f) Privileges and Obligations of Lessees

A lease of salmon fishing is protected by an Act of 1449, Cap. 17 and remains in force even if ownership changes. Unless otherwise provided for in the lease, the following general rules apply:—

15

(i) The local authority rates are payable by the lessee.

(ii) The Fishery Board assessment is payable by the owner.

(iii) The owner of fishings is liable in damages to the lessee, if the subject let suffers injury at the hands of the owner during the currency of the lease.

(iv) The provisions with regard to any subtenants and assignees should be specified.

(v) A lease of fishings conveys to the lessee all rights and privileges belonging to it, as for instance, a right of access to and use of the river bank or adjacent shore.

(vi) The lessee is bound to keep a record of the number of salmon caught and of the species, description and weight, and also the method and date of capture. It is a matter for agreement between owner and lessee as to which of them shall furnish the Secretary of State with such statistics as are required by the *Salmon and Freshwater Fisheries (Protection) (Scotland) Act 1951.* (See Chapter 29).

(g) River Limits

Although disputes about the boundaries of adjoining salmon fisheries have caused much litigation, the law is not entirely settled. The general rules are as follows:—

As between fisheries pertaining to lands adjoining each other on the same bank, the limits are fixed by drawing lines from the land boundaries so as to intersect the centre line or *medium filum* of the river at right angles.

Where fisheries pertain to lands on opposite banks, the general rule depends on whether the river is wide enough to allow the owners of fishings on both banks full exercise of fishing without netting or casting beyond the *medium filum.* In these rivers the boundary is the *medium filum.* In narrower rivers both owners are entitled to fish the whole width of the river, and their competing interests are reconciled either by agreement between them or by regulation imposed by the Court.

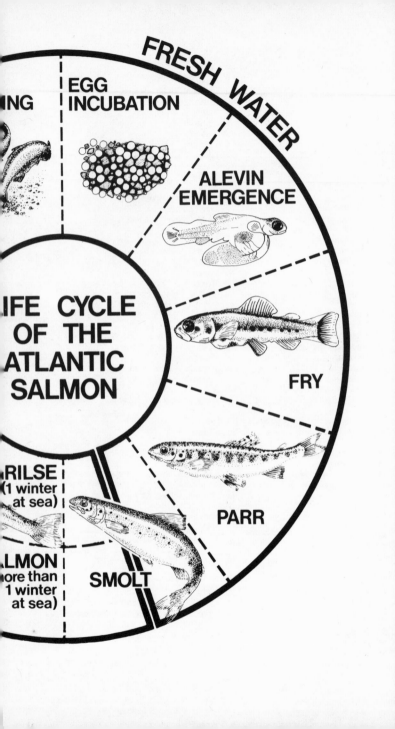

FRESH WATER

...ING

EGG
INCUBATION

ALEVIN
EMERGENCE

LIFE CYCLE
OF THE
ATLANTIC
SALMON

FRY

...RILSE
(1 winter
at sea)

...LMON
...ore than
1 winter
at sea)

PARR

SMOLT

1 Life cycle of the Atlantic salmon

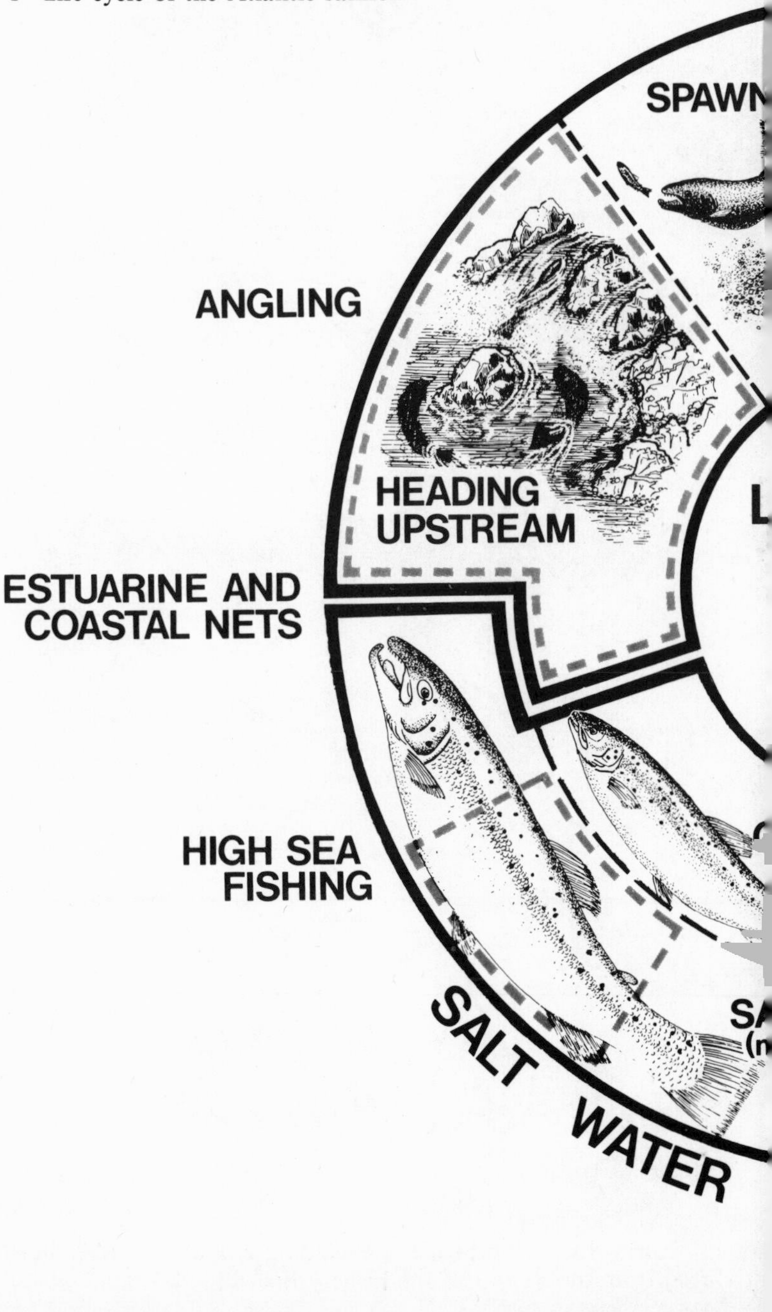

SPAWN

ANGLING

HEADING
UPSTREAM

ESTUARINE AND
COASTAL NETS

HIGH SEA
FISHING

L

SALT WATER

SA
(n

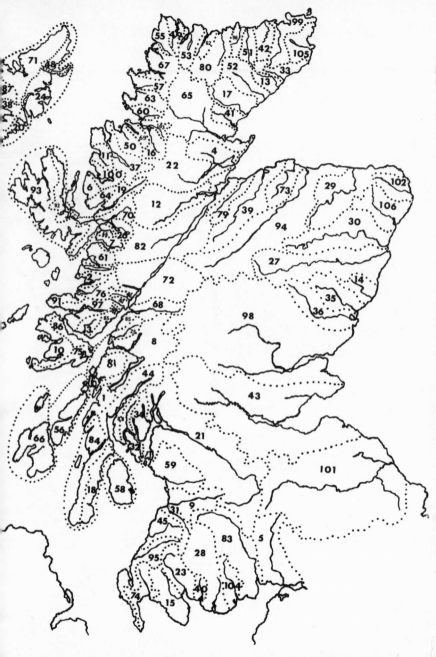

almon fishery districts in Scotland excluding Orkney and Shetland Islands
Produced from the Report of the Fishery Board for Scotland, 1885)

(h) Sea Limits

Under existing international law, national sovereignty extends three miles seawards. In Scotland this is the extent of the right to salmon fishing in the sea. Section 1 of the 1951 Act limits the statutory offence of fishing without permission to any part of the sea within one mile of low water mark. This means that protection to owners and lessees for the area between one and three miles is limited to processes taken under civil law, such as interdict, except in the case of the Tweed (see Chapter 5). Outside the three mile limit there is a general prohibition on fishing for salmon effected by Orders made under powers contained in Sections 5 and 6 of the *Sea Fish (Conservation) Act 1967*. (See Chapter 22).

FURTHER READING

Stewart, C	1892	*The Law of Fishing* (T & T Clark)
Tait, J H	1928	*Game and Fishing Laws of Scotland* (W Green)
Beak, T W	1954	*Salmon and Trout Fishing Law of Scotland* (Gloucester Publications)

4 Legislation—Principal Acts

In some respects the law of salmon fishing is lost in the mists of antiquity and stems from Acts passed by the Scottish Parliament between 1318 and 1705. There are later statutes which regulate in detail the exercise of heritable salmon rights as they are today.

The principal of these are the *Salmon Fisheries (Scotland) Acts* of *1862* and *1868* and the *Salmon and*

Freshwater Fisheries (Protection) (Scotland) Act 1951. The Acts of 1862 and 1868 together provide the basis of salmon law today; the 1951 Act is limited in scope and largely an anti-poaching measure, but does also deal with the weekly close time and the collection of statistics.

Many more Acts regulate particular aspects of salmon fishing and are dealt with in the chapters of this booklet relating to their subjects. However, three more general Acts require special mention. The *Salmon Fisheries (Scotland) Act* of *1828* has been mainly repealed but some sections remain in force although superseded by the later Acts. *The Fishery Boards (Scotland) Act* of *1882* made the Secretary of State for Scotland responsible for the general superintendence of the salmon fisheries of Scotland and for the appointment of an Inspector of Salmon Fisheries. The *Freshwater and Salmon Fisheries (Scotland) Act 1976* is concerned mainly with trout, but there are provisions which bring the penalties for salmon fishing offences up to date, and exempt fish farmers from the prohibitions of various Acts.

The Tweed is covered by the *Tweed Fisheries Act 1857,* the *Tweed Fisheries Amendment Act 1859,* the *Tweed Fisheries Act 1969* and the general Act of 1951. The Solway Firth and its tributaries are governed by the *Solway Act 1804,* and the *Solway Commissioners Act 1877,* and are also largely covered by the general Acts of 1862, 1868 and 1951. There is a valuable report upon the situation in the Solway and its complicated laws contained in an appendix to the *Second Annual Report of the Fishery Board for Scotland 1883.*

5 Special Areas

(a) Tweed

The River Tweed lies partly in Scotland and partly in England. Most of the special legislation affecting the Tweed stems from this fact. There has been special legislation for the River Tweed fisheries since 1771; the principal existing Acts have been named in the preceding paragraph. Under these Acts the administration of the salmon fisheries of the river is the responsibility of the River Tweed Commissioners, whose address is care of A Muir Sturrock, WS, Jedburgh. This body consists of representatives of proprietors of salmon fishings in the river and of representatives appointed by the local authorities in the area. The *Salmon and Freshwater Fisheries (Protection) (Scotland) Act 1951* applies to the whole of the Tweed, including that part which is in England. The mouth of the Tweed has also been the subject of much special legislation. At present the Tweed limits run from Cockburnspath in Berwickshire to Beal Point in Northumberland, and extend five miles seaward.

(b) Solway

The Solway Firth is divided by the national boundary between England and Scotland. The configuration of the bed of the Firth is liable to change and with it the main channel. On the Scottish side eight rivers flow into the Firth and on the English side five. At the head of the Solway the *medium filum* of the River Sark is the boundary between England and Scotland. This applies as far as that point where the Sark joins with the River Esk after which the *medium filum* of the Esk forms the boundary. It has been custom for the Border Esk to be under English law, while the Tweed is subject to Scottish law. When fixed engines on the English side of the Solway were abolished, the *Solway Salmon Fisheries Commissioners (Scotland) Act 1877* was passed to remedy the disparity. The Act provided for the issue of certificates in respect of those fixed engines on the Scottish side which were to be allowed to continue. Today the location and design of Scottish fixed engines on the Solway are still governed by the conditions of these certificates. The Scottish legislation of 1862, 1868 and 1951 applies in other respects to the Scottish waters of the Solway, except the Border Esk. However, the certificate system has left the Solway with an unusual variety of

19

methods of fishing which include poke nets, whammel nets (on the English side), haaf nets and the controversial paidle nets.

(c)   Shetland and Orkney

Many small landowners in Shetland hold their land under udal tenure, a survival of the law which applied when Orkney and Shetland were Norwegian territory. Under udal law the right of salmon fishing is a pertinent of the land and not, as in feudal law which applies to Scotland generally, a separate heritable right. There are no rivers of any size in Shetland, so that nearly all fishing is carried out in the sea. Although there are no net fishings in Orkney, feudal law does not apply there either. Apart from the tenure of the salmon fishing right, the law applying to fisheries in Orkney and Shetland is the same as for the rest of Scotland.

6   District Salmon Fishery Boards

The *Salmon Fisheries (Scotland) Act 1862* provided for the appointment of Commissioners whose duties included the establishment for each river and estuary in Scotland and the coast adjoining thereto of a District as defined by the Commissioners. The statute enacted that for each District there would be a Board consisting of not more than three Upper Proprietors and three Lower Proprietors together with—as chairman—the proprietor having the largest annual valuation. It also specified the voting qualifications, the procedure for the triennial election of the Board and the arrangements where there are fewer than three proprietors from each category. The powers and duties of District Boards were prescribed by Section 22 of the 1862 Act and by Sections 13 and 14 of the *Salmon Fisheries (Scotland) Act 1868*. These sections define the duty of Fishery Boards as being to protect, preserve and improve the fisheries within

20

their districts. The Act of 1868 contained further provisions for administration by District Boards and defined by Schedule such matters as District boundaries, dividing lines between Upper and Lower Proprietors, estuary limits and annual close times.

There are parts of Scotland where no District Boards have been established. A list of the Boards in existence at the date of publication of this booklet is contained in Appendix II. The Hunter Committee (see Chapter 15) recommended that District Salmon Fishery Boards should be replaced by much larger Area Fishery Boards with increased powers and changed membership.

7 Finance

A District Salmon Fishery Board has power under the *Salmon Fisheries (Scotland) Act 1862,* to impose a 'fishery assessment' for the purposes of that Act. The *Salmon Fisheries (Scotland) Act 1868* requires that where a fishery is not entered or is not entered separately in the Valuation Roll, the Regional Assessor must make an entry. That entry is the annual value for the purposes of the fishery assessment.

A Fishery Board fixes its rate of levy annually according to the total amount of revenue it requires to raise in order to meet its financial obligations. The Fishery Board assessment is additional to and separate from local authority rates.

Rod fishings are assessable for local authority rates, but, under the *Local Government and Miscellaneous Financial Provisions (Scotland) Act 1958,* rights of salmon fishing exercised by net or cruive and in respect of which no other revenue is derived by the owner or occupier are exempt from such rates. This exemption does not extend, however, to dwelling houses, bothies, net stores, drying greens, *etc.*

The revenue collected by District Boards is applied towards expenditure on such items as bailiffs' wages, accommodation and transport, hatchery expenses and general work for the protection, preservation and improvement of salmon fisheries.

8 Water Bailiffs

Water Bailiffs are employed by District Salmon Fishery Boards to police the rivers and waters of their districts. Their authority extends to three miles below low water mark and their main powers are set out in the *Salmon Fisheries (Scotland) Act 1868* and the *Salmon and Freshwater Fisheries (Protection) (Scotland) Act 1951.* Persons appointed by the Secretary of State under Section 10(5) of the 1951 Act may exercise the powers of water bailiffs in any waters and the instrument of their appointment constitutes their authority. Water bailiffs may exercise their powers in districts adjoining their own.

(a) Powers of Search

Powers of search under the Salmon Fisheries Acts are now principally contained in Sections 10 and 11 of the 1951 Act, but a small number of powers remain under Sections 26 and 27 of the 1868 Act. A police constable, water bailiff or person appointed by the Secretary of State for the purpose has power to examine any dam, fixed engine, obstruction, or artificial water course, and to enter any land for these purposes. He may also search any boat used in fishing, or suspected of containing salmon or trout, or any net, instrument, fishing basket, pocket, *etc.,* and may seize any fish, instrument, boat, or vehicle liable to forfeiture under the 1951 Act. For these purposes, the term 'water bailiffs' includes bailiffs appointed by the Tweed Commissioners. Anyone who obstructs any of the persons mentioned in carrying out the above duties commits an offence against the 1951 Act.

Under Section 11 of the 1951 Act a Sheriff or Justice of the Peace can issue a warrant if satisfied by evidence on oath that there are reasonable grounds for believing that an offence has been committed under Sections 3 or 4 of the Act. This empowers a police constable, water bailiff or person appointed by the Secretary of State to search any premises or vehicle, or any person found therein, or reasonably suspected of having recently left these premises or vehicle. Section 3 prohibits poaching or illegal fishing by two or more persons, and Section 4 the use of poisons, explosives or electrical devices for taking salmon or trout. If due to urgency, there is no time to obtain a warrant, a police constable may search a vehicle if he has reasonable grounds for believing that it contains evidence of the commission of an offence against either Sections 3 or 4 of the 1951 Act. On similar grounds of urgency, a water bailiff or person appointed by the Secretary of State may search a vehicle, provided it is on private land adjoining water.

Section 26 of the 1868 Act, as amended by the 1951 Act, gives power to search by warrant where there is evidence of a breach of the provisions of that Act, but in this case the powers do not extend to vehicles. The most important of the provisions still remaining under the 1868 Act are annual close time and associated measures, use of nets of illegal mesh, and the provisions with regard to obstructions, mill dams, weirs, and cruives.

Section 27 of the 1868 Act gives water bailiffs and police constables powers of entry to private land for the purpose of preventing offences under that Act. These powers may now be exercised to prevent offences against the 1951 Act also. If challenged, however, by the proprietor they must quit unless they are able to prove that they had a good reason to believe that a breach of the law has been, or is about to be, committed.

(b) Powers of Arrest

The *Salmon and Freshwater Fisheries (Protection) (Scotland) Act 1951* limits the powers of arrest for offences under the Salmon Fisheries Acts to police, water bailiffs, and persons appointed by the Secretary of State. This

23

limitation applies not only to offences under the 1951 Act, but is extended by Section 12 of that Act to offences under the *Salmon Fisheries (Scotland) Act 1868* and the *Tweed Fisheries Acts 1857* and *1859*. It should be noted that a water bailiff is defined under the 1951 Act as 'a water bailiff or other duly appointed officer of a District Board', and a District Board is defined as a District Board constituted under the provisions of the *Salmon Fisheries (Scotland) Acts* or the *Tweed Fisheries Acts*. By Section 10(3) a bailiff on production of his warrant of appointment is empowered to carry out his duties under the Acts. A water bailiff's powers of arrest extend to offences under Part I of the 1951 Act, and to those Sections of the 1868 Act which are detailed in Section 29 of that Act as amended by the 1951 Act. Water bailiffs appointed by the Tweed Commissioners have powers of arrest for offences under Part I of the 1951 Act and under the *Tweed Fisheries Acts* of *1857* and *1859*.

The main offences for which the offenders are subject to arrest are broadly fishing for salmon without legal right or written permission; fishing by illegal methods; certain illegal fishing by two or more persons acting together; use of explosives, poisons and electrical devices; unauthorised removal of dead salmon or trout; fishing for salmon in the annual close season, other than by rod and line; fishing in the weekly close time, other than by rod and line; fishing on Sundays by rod and line; fishing for salmon by rod and line during the close season contrary to bye-law provisions; using a net with mesh contrary to bye-law provisions; using a net to catch salmon at waterfalls, *etc*; preventing the passage of or catching salmon at fish passes; buying, selling or possessing salmon roe; buying, selling or possessing young salmon; disturbing spawn; buying, selling, taking or possessing unclean or unseasonable salmon; and buying, or selling, or having in possession, salmon taken in the close season.

(c) Prosecutions

In Scotland all salmon fishing offences are reported to the Procurator Fiscal who undertakes any ensuing prosecution unless there is express statutory provision to the

24

contrary. The 1951 Act makes no provision for private prosecution, so that for offences which are contrary to this Act prosecution can only be made at the instance of the Procurator Fiscal. District Boards and private parties including the Fishmongers' Company can prosecute for offences which still fall under the 1868 Act. In the Tweed District the Tweed Commissioners or their Superintendent can prosecute for offences against the Tweed Fisheries Acts.

(d) Penalties

Penalties for poaching and illegal fishing are now contained mainly in the *Freshwater and Salmon Fisheries (Scotland) Act 1976* but the penalties for some offences under the 1868 Act and the Tweed Acts are covered by these Acts.

9 Annual and Weekly Close Times

(a) Annual Close Time

(*i*) *General* The annual close time is 168 days except for the River Tweed where it is 153 days. It is universally applicable to every method of fishing for salmon in any river, loch or estuary, or in the sea, but with variations for rod and line fishing. The actual dates can vary from District to District and can be altered from time to time on application to the Secretary of State. A complete statement of the present close times for the Scottish rivers is in Appendix II. The differences are based on the assumption that the spawning season is later in some rivers than in others.

(*ii*) *Rod Fishing* During certain periods fixed for each District, either before or after the annual close time, it is lawful to fish for salmon by rod and line. (See Appendix II).

25

26

3 Net and Coble

(*iii*) *Net Fishing* The occupier of any fishery must within 36 hours from the commencement of the annual close time, remove all gear from the fishery and adjacent landing places. He must effectually secure the gear so as to prevent it being used until the end of the close time.

(*iv*) *Offences* Apart from fishing for salmon during the annual close time, or not removing gear from a fishery, there are three other offences. It is an offence to obstruct salmon in their passage to any spawning bed during the close time. It is an offence to buy, sell, or possess salmon during the period from the start of the latest close time to the end of the earliest close time, not including the rod fishing extension, unless the person concerned can prove the fish were taken legitimately. Fish farmers are exempted from this last provision by the *Freshwater and Salmon Fisheries (Scotland) Act 1976.* Finally it is an offence to export salmon caught by rod and line during the close time for net fishing unless their legal capture can be certified.

(b) Weekly Close Time

(*i*) *General* The weekly close time applicable to every method of fishing is fixed by the *Salmon and Freshwater Fisheries (Protection) (Scotland) Act 1951.*

(*ii*) *Rod Fishing* The weekly close time for rod fishing is Sunday.

(*iii*) *Net Fishing* The weekly close time for methods of fishing other than rod and line, is from twelve noon on Saturday to six o'clock on the following Monday morning. To comply with the weekly close time, stake nets must have a clear opening or outlet four feet wide from top to bottom. Fly nets must either be raised or lowered so as effectually to prevent the capture of salmon. Bag nets must have their leaders removed.

(*iv*) *Offences* Failure to perform the required operations, or fishing during the weekly close time are offences. Impossibility to comply owing to wind and weather is a valid excuse for the fisherman but if later during the weekly close time it is possible to put the nets out of action, this must be done. Difficulty in putting the nets out of action owing to the state of the tide is not a valid defence.

Fish farmers are exempted by the *Freshwater and Salmon Fisheries (Scotland) Act 1976* in respect of fish farm working.

10 Legal Methods of Salmon Fishing

Methods permissible under the Salmon Fishery Acts are net fishing, rod fishing and (under charter) cruive fishing; persons using these methods must have the legal right or written permission from the owner or the lessee of the fishings. As a general restriction, Schedule E of the *Salmon Fisheries (Scotland) Act 1868* stipulates that in net fishing the minimum legal mesh size is seven inches all round when the net is wet. Landing nets used in rod fishing are exempted from this restriction.

(a) Methods within Estuary Limits

(*i*) *Net and Coble* is the only method of netting permitted within the estuary limits. These limits, however, as shown in Schedule B of the 1868 Act, delineate only the seaward limits of the estuaries, and the inland waters so contained may include sea water lochs, rivers and freshwater lochs. Legal net and coble fishing must comply with certain rules which have been established by precedent in the Scottish Courts. These decisions require that the net must not leave the hand of the fisherman and must be kept in motion relative to the water while fishing. The construction of the net must also show that it is designed to encircle the fish and not merely to enmesh them.

(*ii*) *Cruives* are a form of trap used very rarely and then only by the holders of cruive charter rights. General regulations with respect to the construction and use of cruives are set out in Schedule F of the 1868 Act.

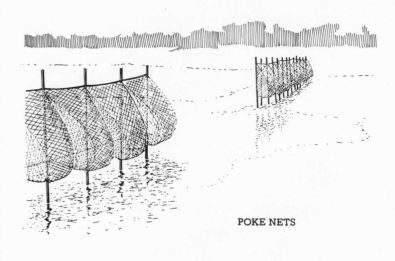

POKE NETS

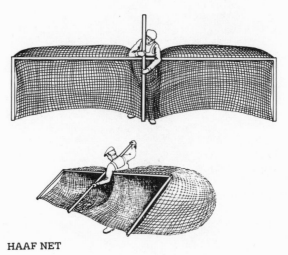

HAAF NET

4 Special nets used on the Solway

30

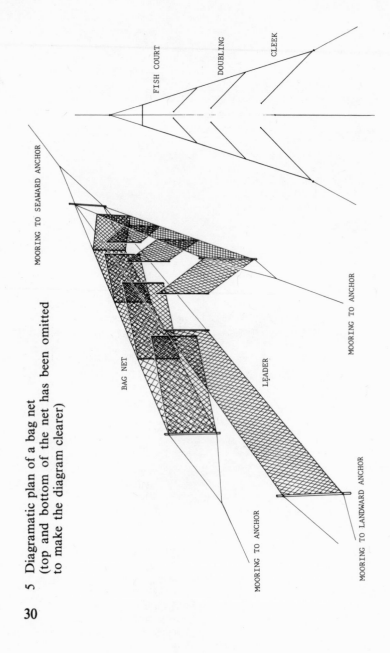

5 Diagramatic plan of a bag net
(top and bottom of the net has been omitted
to make the diagram clearer)

(*iii*) *Rod and Line* fishing is a legal method of fishing in all salmon fishings and, under the *Salmon and Freshwater Fisheries (Protection) (Scotland) Act 1951,* it is defined as a single rod and line with such bait or lure as is lawful at the passing of the Act. (For illegal baits and lures, see Chapter 11).

(*iv*) *Certificated Fixed Engines* are a privileged method of fishing in the Solway Firth, under the *Solway Commissioners Act 1877.*

(b) Methods outwith Estuary Limits

(*i*) *Fixed Engines*

The Bag net may be defined as a net extending seawards from the shore, suspended from floats and anchored in a fixed position. It consists of a trap made of netting to which fish are directed by a leader of netting. The purpose of the leader is to lead fish towards and into the trap. The leader does not usually exceed 120 metres in length. One end of the leader is attached to the trap and the other securely fixed either to the shore or the seabed. The material of which the leader is made is of sufficient thickness to be visible to the fish and to demonstrate clearly the intention of leading fish into the trap or guiding them towards it and not itself enmeshing fish. No part of the trap netting should be of thinner material than the leader. Bag nets are often shot in a line seawards from the end of a shore attached bag net or stake net.

The *Stake net* or *Fly net* is a net fixed to the foreshore by stakes. It may be defined as a curtain of netting erected on stakes, set vertically in the foreshore, which acts as a leader to approaching salmon with a pocket or trap inserted at intervals to take fish which are directed along the leader. It is fixed to the foreshore throughout its length. The purpose of the leader is to lead fish toward and into the pocket or trap. The netting is of sufficient thickness to be visible to fish and to demonstrate clearly the intention of leading fish into the pocket or trap or guiding fish towards them and is not itself designed to enmesh fish.

The *Jumper net* is a type of fly net where the stakes and netting of the leader are replaced by a floating curtain of

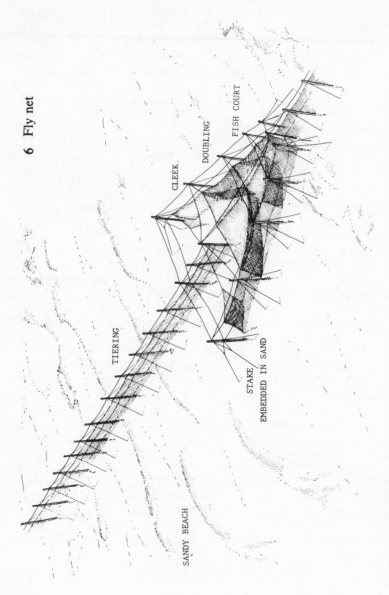

TIERING

CLEEK.

DOUBLING

FISH COURT

STAKE
EMBEDDED IN SAND

SANDY BEACH

netting which is fixed at both ends and which rises and falls with the tide.

(*ii*) *Beach Seine Netting* is the term sometimes used for net and coble fishing practised outside estuary limits and the restrictions for net and coble fishing, so far as relevant, apply.

(*iii*) *Rod and Line* fishing is a legal method as defined under paragraph (a)(*iii*) above.

(*iv*) *Nets of special construction,* and including certificated fixed engines, are used in the Solway. The legislation regulating these is contained mainly in the Solway Acts.

11 Illegal Methods of Salmon Fishing

(a)   Rivers and Inland Waters within Estuary Limits

Net and coble and rod and line are the only legal methods other than the certificated fixed engines of the Solway and the cruives sanctioned by ancient charter in two or three rivers. All other methods are illegal. Other methods of fishing may, however, be used for scientific purposes in special circumstances but the permission of the District Fishery Board and of the proprietor is required or where there is no District Fishery Board the permission of the Secretary of State for Scotland. The best known illegal method of rod fishing is snatching or sniggering. This method has long been prohibited—originally by Section 17 of the *Salmon Fisheries (Scotland) Act 1968,* and following the repeal of that Section, by Sections 2 and 24(2) of the *Salmon and Freshwater Fisheries (Protection) (Scotland) Act 1951.* The use of salmon roe as a bait or lure when fishing is an offence under the 1868 Act.

(b)   Outwith Estuary Limits

The use of drift nets to enmesh salmon was banned in Scottish coastal waters on the recommendation of the Committee on Scottish Salmon and Trout Fisheries in their First Report of July 1963. (See Chapter 15). The *Salmon and Migratory Trout (Prohibition of Fishing) (No. 2) Order 1972,* the *Salmon and Migratory Trout (North East Atlantic) Order 1972,* the *Salmon and Migratory Trout (North West Atlantic) Order 1971* and the *Salmon and Migratory Trout (Restrictions on Landing) Order 1972* have extended the ban both on fishing for salmon and the landing of drift net caught salmon in Great Britain. In addition methods prohibited within the limits of a specified area off the coast of Scotland and the Tweed now include drift net or other gill net worked from a boat, trawl net, seine net, troll or long line. Originally the banned area was the 12 mile coastal band of Scotland but that has now been extended to the whole North Atlantic. The use of boat-operated gill nets, being curtains of netting anchored to the seabed or the foreshore and designed to enmesh fish, is banned by the *Salmon and Migratory Trout (Prohibition of Fishing) Amendment Order 1975.* This method of fishing is illegal if a boat is used at any stage of the setting or operation of the net. The landing of fish caught in this manner is banned by the *Salmon and Migratory Trout (Restrictions on Landing) Amendment Order 1975.* All these Orders are Statutory Instruments made under the *Sea Fish (Conservation) Act 1967.*

(c)   In Any Waters

The use of small mesh nets, explosives, poisons, noxious substances, otters, any light or fire, spears, leisters, gaffs or similar instruments, and electrical devices to take or destroy salmon is illegal. Deliberate interference with a neighbour's rights are among other practices not allowed. The taking of dead salmon or trout from any waters is an offence unless by persons authorised to do so. Gaffs are allowed only when used as an aid to landing fish when angling. The taking of salmon by otherwise illegal means is permissible, however, where consent has been given by an

34

appropriate authority in the interest of scientific or development work. Section 9 of the 1951 Act also gives District Salmon Fishery Boards immunity for the purpose of protecting, improving or developing stocks of fish.

(d) Prosecutions

Illegal methods of fishing are the subject of Crown prosecutions with the exception of offences involving kelts, unseasonable fish, *etc,* which still come within the terms of the 1868 Act and may be the subject of a private prosecution.

12 Consignment and Marketing Regulations

(a) Provisions of 1951 Act

Section 16 of the *Salmon and Freshwater Fisheries (Protection) (Scotland) Act 1951* requires packages of salmon, sea trout and trout sent by any common or other carrier to be marked under penalty with the words 'salmon', 'sea trout' or 'trout', and gives power to specified persons to open packages suspected of containing these fish.

(b) Trade Descriptions Act 1968

The *Labelling of Food Regulations 1967, Statutory Instrument No. 1864,* made under the *Food and Drugs Act 1955,* gives the appropriate designations of fish in Schedule 1. Thus only the species *Salmo salar* has the appropriate designation of 'salmon' and the various Pacific salmon (*Oncorhynchus*) must be designated 'sockeye salmon', 'coho salmon', 'chinook salmon', 'chum salmon', *etc.* The *Trade Descriptions Act 1968* prohibits under penalty the false description of goods provided in the course of trade.

13 Common Law Water Rights

The Common Law principles applicable to the flow of water in a river are as follows:

(a) While all riparian proprietors have a common interest in the water, none of them has an exclusive right of property in it.

(b) Subject to the qualifications noted below, no proprietor may use the water or affect its flow in a manner prejudicial to the interests of others.

(c) Unless sanctioned by statute, the impounding of water by a riparian proprietor may be challenged by a downstream proprietor.

(d) All riparian proprietors may take water for such primary uses as watering stock and domestic purposes even though this absorbs all or part of the supply available to downstream proprietors.

(e) No proprietor may take water for other purposes, such as irrigation or manufacturing processes, if the result is to infringe the reasonable rights of any downstream proprietor.

(f) A proprietor may also stop operations by an upstream proprietor which cause a material change in the quality of water flowing down. This does not apply, however, to operations relating to ordinary estate management.

14 Research

The Secretary of State for Scotland has power to conduct inquiries and investigations into questions of practical or scientific importance to salmon and freshwater fisheries. Research on salmon in Scotland is mainly conducted by the Department of Agriculture and Fisheries for Scotland at the Freshwater Fisheries Laboratory at Faskally, Pitlochry, Perthshire, with outstations at Ballater (Aberdeenshire Dee), Montrose (North Esk) and Almondbank (Tay), all under the general supervision of the Director of Fisheries Research for Scotland. The Laboratory's main object is to undertake research on the biology of salmon as a basis for advising government on their conservation, protection and rational exploitation.

Investigations into the biology of salmon have been undertaken by the Laboratory since 1950. These have included the study of juvenile stocks in selected rivers, the migration of smolts from these rivers, the subsequent return of adult salmon to spawn and the relationship between spawning stock and juvenile production. Migrating smolts are counted and tagged for subsequent identification while adults are counted when returning to spawn. Age determinations are routinely made on both juvenile and adult fish by scale reading. Catches of salmon and sea trout taken by rods and nets are reported annually to the Department by all fishery proprietors as required by the *Salmon and Freshwater Fisheries (Protection) (Scotland) Act 1951,* providing a census of the numbers of fish taken in Scottish waters. A proportion of the commercial net catches is sampled in some rivers, to examine the age composition of the adult stocks entering these rivers.

Studies are also made of the relative abundance of the juvenile stages of salmon in selected rivers, and its dependence on living space and food supply. The smolt rearing station at Almondbank provides controlled conditions for studying the factors governing the production of smolts in hatcheries and the release conditions for maximum survival to adults, in relation to the improvement of salmon stocks. Investigations are made into the contamination of fish by various pollutants, and of the chemicals responsible for fish mortalities. Research on salmon diseases is carried out at the Department's Marine Laboratory, Victoria Road, Torry, Aberdeen. Research on seal damage to salmon fisheries is conducted jointly by the Freshwater and Marine Fisheries Laboratories. Information and advice on the scientific aspects of freshwater fisheries, especially relating to their management, is provided by the Freshwater Fisheries Laboratory.

The results of the research of the DAFS laboratories are published in various scientific journals, but a brief account appears in *Fisheries of Scotland,* the annual report of the Department. The Pitlochry laboratory published a separate annual report of its work until 1972, but triennial reviews of the Laboratory's work are due to be produced in future, the first covering the period 1973-75. Reprints of scientific papers published by the Pitlochry staff can sometimes be obtained from the Laboratory, or the appropriate scientific journals can be borrowed from public libraries.

Work on the processing, handling and storage of salmon has been done by the Torry Research Station in Aberdeen. Additional research on disease is undertaken by the Aquatic Pathobiology Unit at Stirling University and on the distribution of young salmon in streams at the Department of Forestry and Natural Resources at Edinburgh University. Work on acclimatisation of salmon smolts in sea water has been done by the Scottish Marine Biological Association at Oban. Salmon farming research by various organisations is being carried out or is in contemplation.

FURTHER READING

Menzies, W J M	1926	*General Index to the Reports and Papers issued by the Fishery Board for Scotland 1882-1924* (HMSO)
Pyefinch, K A	1955	*A Review of the Literature on the Biology of the Atlantic Salmon* (HMSO)
DAFS	1973	*Directorate of Fisheries Research Report for 1972* (HMSO)
DAFS	1977	*Triennial Review of Freshwater Fisheries Research 1973-75*

15 The Hunter Committee

A Committee, under the chairmanship of Lord Hunter, was appointed by the Secretary of State for Scotland in March, 1962, to review the law relating to salmon and trout fisheries in Scotland, including the Tweed, with special reference to the constitution, powers and functions of District Boards, and the responsibilities of the Secretary of State, and to consider in the light of current scientific knowledge the extent to which fishing for salmon and trout by any method, whether in inland waters or in the sea should be regulated, and to recommend such changes in the law as might be thought desirable.

At that time, drift net fishing for salmon off the east coast of Scotland, which had started in 1960, was developing rapidly and there were fears in some quarters that salmon stocks might be endangered. The Committee gave priority to this subject and in a First Report published in July 1963 (Command 2096) *Scottish Salmon and Trout Fisheries* recommended a prohibition of drift net fishing reinforced by a ban on landings of drift net caught fish. The Government subsequently implemented this recommendation by introducing the appropriate Orders. These Orders have been renewed as they expired and the prohibition is still in force.

The Second Report of the Committee, published in August 1965, (Command 2691) *Scottish Salmon and Trout Fisheries,* made far-reaching recommendations for the regulation and management of salmon fisheries. These recommendations were subsequently the subject of much consultation and discussion but have not so far been implemented.

In November 1971, however, the government published a White Paper (Command 4821) *Salmon and Freshwater Fisheries in Scotland,* giving proposals for action arising from the Hunter Committee.

16 Salmon Culture

(a) Hatcheries

The rearing of brown and rainbow trout and Atlantic salmon for stocking purposes has been practised in Scotland for a long time, and hatchery techniques for the three species are essentially the same. Eggs are stripped from ripe females, fertilised by sperm from males, and are either planted out some months later as eyed ova or hatched in trays or troughs to the fry stage. Unfed salmon fry may be used for stocking a little before the point of complete absorption of the yolk sac and this eliminates the cost of feeding; or else the fry may be fed for a few weeks before planting in nursery streams. Nursery areas which are naturally inaccessible to migratory fish are often prepared for planting by the removal of stocks of undesirable species of fish which may be predators or competitors.

(b) Smolt Rearing

When a river is fully stocked by natural or artificial means, the only way of increasing its production is by rearing fry to the smolt stage. These fish can then be released at the time of migration to saltwater, in the hope that their eventual return as adult fish will justify the cost of rearing them to the smolt stage. So far the high costs of producing smolts artificially and the low return as adults has made smolt culture economically justifiable only in exceptional circumstances.

(c) Marine Farming

In recent years developments have taken place on the west coast of Scotland in the sea cage cultivation of salmon. Smolts reared in freshwater hatcheries are transferred to sea water cages in sheltered locations where they grow to marketable size. These developments are still in their early stages, and the total production of farmed salmon is currently quite small.

FURTHER READING

Carlin, B	1960	*A Swedish View of the Value of Stocking Rivers with Salmon* (Salmon & Trout Assn.)
Piggins, D J	1968	*Salmon Hatching and Rearing Techniques* (The Salmon Research Trust of Ireland)
Anderson, J I W	1973	*Salmon Farming in Scotland* (Salmon & Trout Association)

17 Fish Counters

The Hunter Committee (see Chapter 15) recommend that, for efficient management of salmon stocks, a knowledge of spawning escapement was vital and suggested that commercial river traps would provide this information, but the recommendations have not been implemented. Fish counters, sited above the main commercial or rod fisheries in salmon rivers, would be suitable for this purpose.

The existing types are:

(a) The *resistivity counter,* detecting a change in the conductivity of the water between electrodes as a fish passes.

(b) The *sonar counter,* transmitting sound waves and detecting echoes from fish.

(c) The *Sharkey Delta Vee counter,* detecting minute electrical disturbances in the muscles of a swimming fish.

The potential of the Delta Vee counter is thought to be limited as it is very sensitive to electrical 'noise' in the environment. Both the resistivity and the sonar counter show promise, although the former has been more fully tested. They must both be installed in fast flowing water, so that fish do not linger in the counting zone and produce false counts. Both are sensitive to turbulence; and air bubbles and obstacles such as rocks interfere with the sonar counter. Resistivity counters can be installed in tubes or open channels, or sited on the downstream faces of weirs, obviating the need for fish to enter a tube or channel. Sonar counters work best across the crest of a submerged weir where the velocity encourages the fish to cross the counter beam positively.

FURTHER READING

Department of the Environment: *A Review of Fish*
Water Data Unit 1975   *Counter Development*

18 River Maintenance

(a) Responsibility for River Improvement

The *Salmon Fisheries (Scotland) Act 1868* gives Fishery Boards power to purchase by agreement for the purpose of removal, any dam dyke or other fixed engine, for the benefit of the fisheries, and to remove any natural obstructions to the passage of fish or to instal a fish pass at any waterfall. The Boards have power to protect or improve the fisheries within their District. In consultation with riparian owners and salmon fishery proprietors, they may take measures to increase the stocks of salmon. It is also open to individual proprietors to take steps to improve their own fisheries.

(b) Stock Improvement

Each area of water is capable of supporting a limited number of young salmon. One way to increase the salmon production of a river is to open more of it to the spawning activities of adult salmon. Any suitable spawning or nursery area to which mature fish cannot penetrate represents so much lost potential unless it can be stocked artificially. Hatcheries can provide the ova or unfed fry to stock these unutilised areas of rivers, and so bring the whole river up to maximum production. The stocking of parts of rivers which are already adequately populated by wild salmon is of doubtful value.

(c) Improvement

The important question as to whether salmon lie in a certain part of a river, often depends on the extent to which a proprietor looks after his section of the river banks. In areas where nothing is done and unstable banks continually crumble into the river, the result may be shallow pools that do not hold fish. On the other hand the strengthening and consolidation of banks, especially on the outside of bends, will tend to deepen pools at these points. The provision of low groynes to direct the flow of water can also be helpful, but as water tends to flow at right angles over a groyne, the angle at which the groyne is set to the bank is of the greatest importance.

(d) Gravel Abstraction

Under common law a fishery proprietor is protected against injurious interference with the natural course of the river. It has been held that where a proprietor's interest in maintaining the ordinary course of the river has been infringed through the removal of gravel, the person who has removed that gravel must replace it and restore the natural course of the river. A proprietor can stop such interference by means of an interdict. Under Section 19 of the 1868 Act it is an offence to disturb any spawning bed or any bank or shallow containing salmon spawn.

(e) Impoundment to Regulate Flow

A fishery proprietor may wish to dam a stream in order to store water which may be released at times of dry weather to supplement low water flows. In this case he should seek the approval of other interested proprietors, remembering their common law rights (see Chapter 13). If the dam is in a stream frequented by salmon, it must afford a reasonable means for the passage of migratory fish and the regulations detailed in Schedule G of the *Salmon Fisheries (Scotland) Act 1868* should be observed. If the impoundment created is a reservoir capable of holding more than five million gallons of water above the natural level, a qualified civil engineer must supervise the construction and it is subject to other provisions contained in the *Reservoirs (Safety Provisions) Act 1930*.

FURTHER READING

Menzies, W J M   1934   *Salmon Passes—Their Design and Construction* (HMSO)

44

Clay, C H	1961	*Design of Fishways and Other Fish Facilities* (Dept. of Fisheries, Ottawa)
Mills, D H	1964	*The Ecology of the Young Stages of Atlantic Salmon in the River Bran, Ross-shire* (HMSO)
Egglishaw, H J	1970	Production of Salmon and Trout in a Stream in Scotland (*J. Fish. Biol. 2,* 117-136)
Fort, R S and Brayshaw, J D	1961	*Fishery Management* (Faber & Faber)

19 Water Abstraction

(a) The Law

(*i*) Water authorities in Scotland have powers under section 21 of the *Water (Scotland) Act 1946* to acquire by agreement, or compulsorily, right to take water from any stream or other source.

(*ii*) These powers relate to public water supplies only; abstractions from rivers by riparian owners (and by other persons who may have similar rights) are not generally subject to statutory control. Spray irrigation in Scotland can be controlled under the *Spray Irrigation (Scotland) Act 1964,* which empowers River Purification Boards to apply to the Secretary of State for a control order. When a control order is applied to any area, anyone wishing to abstract water for spray irrigation must apply to the Purification Board for a licence, and this can be suspended during a water shortage.

(*iii*) Section 18(4) of the *Rivers (Prevention of Pollution) (Scotland) Act 1951* provides that a River Purification Board may require a person abstracting substantial quantities of water to furnish such information as the Board may specify.

(*iv*) The *Rivers (Prevention of Pollution) (Scotland) Acts 1951* and *1965* contain powers to control the quality, volume and location of discharges of industrial and sewage effluents to rivers and certain tidal waters.

(*v*) The statutory powers of District Fishery Boards with regard to abstraction are limited to the powers to regulate mill lades under Schedule G of the *Salmon Fisheries (Scotland) Act 1868*. At Common Law, District Fishery Boards may sue in the name of their Clerks although they have no title to sue for interdict. They may object to the abstraction proposals of public water undertakings and in some cases this may result in a Public Inquiry.

(b) Types of Abstraction

(*i*) Water taken and quickly returned to the river system unimpaired in quantity and quality, *eg* hydro-electric impoundments, water power installation, amenity water courses and ponds, reservoirs for fire fighting, *etc.*

(*ii*) Water taken and returned to the river reduced in quantity or altered in quality, *eg* fish farming, industrial processes, industrial cooling water, sand and gravel washing, *etc.*

(*iii*) Water taken and returned only at some unrelated time, or diverted to another catchment, *eg* water supplies, spray irrigation, chemical crop spraying, hydro-electric diversions, process water discharged to sewers, *etc.* (See Chapter 13).

(*iv*) Water taken by bore hole abstraction. This is subject to some control under section 4 of the *Water (Scotland) Act 1946*.

(c) Fish Screens and Hecks

The protection of immature fish, particularly smolts during the time of migration, is important and is regulated by Schedules F and G of the *Salmon Fisheries (Scotland) Act 1868*. Plans for fish screens at intakes may be examined by interested parties. Hecks at points of discharge are necessary where there is a danger of migratory fish ascending the discharge instead of the main stream.

46

20 Pollution

(a) The Law

(*i*) The principal Act governing control of river pollution in Scotland is the *Rivers (Prevention of Pollution) (Scotland) Act 1951,* which centralised authority in the Secretary of State and provided for an Advisory Committee and River Purification Boards.

(*ii*) Important changes in the law were made by the *Rivers (Prevention of Pollution) (Scotland) Act 1965* which extended control to many previously uncontrolled discharges. New or altered outlets and new discharges to certain tidal waters were also brought under control.

(*iii*) The *Control of Pollution Act 1974* contains further provisions for the prevention of pollution of water. It contains additional powers to control river pollution and when it comes into operation, will in the main replace the 1951 and 1965 Acts.

(*iv*) The *River Purification Board Areas (Scotland) Order 1975* reconstituted River Purification Boards and established new boundaries. For the first time these boards cover the whole of mainland Scotland.

(b) Procedure

If pollution is suspected, the appropriate River Purification Board should be contacted immediately. In many cases the District Fishery Board should also be informed. Addresses and telephone numbers of the River Purification Boards of Scotland are listed in Appendix VI. If neither Purification Board nor District Fishery Board can be contacted, the police should be informed.

(c) Pollution Control

It is the duty of River Purification Boards to promote

the cleanliness of all waters in their areas, and to achieve this they set standards for all discharges to which they give consent. The Anglers' Co-operative Association helps its members with civil claims for damages resulting from pollution. Advice can be sought from the Scottish River Purification Advisory Committee in the case of persistent pollution or where a River Purification Board has not apparently taken action. They can be contacted care of the Scottish Development Department, Edinburgh.

(d) Fish Hatcheries

Fish hatcheries must obtain consent to discharge their effluent which must conform to standards required by the River Purification Board. The water supply must be of high quality, and careful control must be maintained to prevent the outbreak of disease.

21 Disease

The two commonest endemic diseases affecting wild salmon stocks in Scotland are furunculosis, which appears occasionally in isolated outbreaks in summer during high temperature and lower water conditions, and ulcerative dermal necrosis (UDN). The latter appeared in Scotland in 1966 although a similar disease was recorded towards the end of the last century. Epizootics of UDN have resulted in substantial mortalities among mature adult fish but a proportion of the stock survives and populations have never been eliminated.

Those concerned with the management of salmon fisheries must always be vigilant in the matter of disease among fish. The spread of disease can be aggravated by the introduction of fish from a contaminated source.

The *Diseases of Fish Act 1937* and the *Diseases of Fish Order 1973* grant powers to the Secretary of State for

Scotland 'to prevent the spreading of disease among salmon and freshwater fish'. Under the Act and relative Orders as at present enacted, nine diseases of ecological or economic importance are notifiable. In practice these are reported to the Department of Agriculture and Fisheries for Scotland at the Marine Laboratory, Aberdeen, where officers are responsible for disease identification. District Salmon Fishery Boards who have grounds for suspecting the presence of a notifiable disease in their waters (but excluding fish farms) must report the facts to the Marine Laboratory.

The Act empowers the Secretary of State to impose an Infected Area Order (IAO) on natural waters and fish farms where evidence has shown the presence of a notifiable disease. The powers are discretionary, and at their strongest they prevent the movement of live fish and other infected materials outwith the area of the Order. Fishery Boards may be required, where an IAO is placed, to keep a record of diseased fish removed; however, in practice, IAOs have been confined to fish farms. At present seven of the nine notifiable diseases relate to salmon, *viz* infectious pancreatic necrosis (IPN), whirling disease (WD), viral haemorrhagic septicemia (VHS), infectious haematopoietic necrosis (IHN), furunculosis, columnaris and UDN; over the past ten years, UDN has been the major cause of fish mortalities.

FURTHER READING

Roberts, R J and Shepherd, C J   1975   *Handbook of Trout and Salmon Diseases.* (Fishing News Books Ltd.)

22 High Seas Salmon Fisheries

A localised salmon fishery in west Greenland developed into a significant autumn inshore set gillnet fishery in the 1960s, exceeding 1,500 tonnes by 1965. An offshore drift net fishery also developed from that time and the combined annual catch exceeded 2,000 tonnes from 1969 to 1973, when regulations limiting the quantities of salmon caught in this fishery were introduced by the North West Atlantic Fisheries Commission. Tagging showed that these fish would return as salmon to both North American and European rivers.

A major long line fishery for salmon developed in the Norwegian Sea outside Norwegian fishery limits in the mid 1960s. By 1970 the catch reached almost 1,000 tonnes, but was subsequently regulated to half the size. Tagging showed that most fish returned to Norwegian and, to a lesser extent, to Russian rivers. An exploratory fishery round the Faroes has shown that some fish feeding in this area return to Britain or Scandinavia as grilse.

The North-East Atlantic Fisheries Commission in 1970 imposed limitations on the Norwegian Sea Fishery, while in 1972 the International Council for Northwest Atlantic Fisheries phased out the offshore fishery at Greenland over the four years ending 31st December, 1975, and restricted the Greenland inshore catch to 1,100 tonnes. This quota was re-calculated at 1,191 tonnes per annum in 1974. The *Salmon and Migratory Trout (North East Atlantic) Order 1972* prohibited all British vessels from fishing for salmon in the NEAFC area outside the fishery limits of the British Isles from February, 1973, to February, 1983, (see Chapter 11). Appendix I sets out the West Greenland catch figures from 1960 to 1975.

FURTHER READING

Report of the ICES/ICNAF Joint Working Party on North Atlantic Salmon, 1966. *International Council for the Exploration of the Sea, Co-operative Research Report, Series A, No. 8.*

Report of the ICES/ICNAF Joint Working Party on North Atlantic Salmon, May, 1968. *International Council for the Exploration of the Sea, Co-operative Research Report, Series A, No. 12.*

Report of the ICES/ICNAF Joint Working Party on North Atlantic Salmon, December, 1970. *International Council for the Exploration of the Sea, Co-operative Research Report, Series A, No. 24.*

Pyefinch, K A   1971   Atlantic Salmon in the Sea (*Proc. Roy. Soc. Edin. (B) 73, 423-428.*)

Parrish, B B   1973   A Review of the Work of the ICES/ICNAF Joint Working Party on North Atlantic Salmon (*International Atlantic Salmon Foundation*)

Report of the ICES/ICNAF Joint Working Party on North Atlantic Salmon, November, 1973. *International Council for the Exploration of the Sea, Co-operative Research Report No. 35.*

Parrish, B B   1977   West Greenland Salmon
Horsted Sv. Aa. and   Fishery: Biology of Resources
May, A W   and Effects of Fishing. *Rapp. Cons. Explor. Mer.*

23 Predation and Damage to Salmon

(a) Predators

Seals, cormorants, goosanders, mergansers and gulls are among the principal predators of salmon. Although some of these species are subject to varying degrees of protection, District Boards and proprietors or their agents can take steps to control predators if they are destroying salmon or interfering with fishing gear. Pike, brown trout, eels, and some species of sea fish are also predators at various life stages of the salmon.

(b)   Destruction of Young Salmon

The young of salmon are protected by Section 19 of the *Salmon Fisheries (Scotland) Act 1868*. This section makes it an offence to take or destroy any smolt or salmon fry, or to buy, sell, or possess the same for sale. It also specifies exceptions including artificial propagation, scientific purposes, and certain works in a river.

(c)   Disturbance of Spawning Beds

Spawning beds are protected by Section 19 of the 1868 Act. This section makes it an offence wilfully to disturb or destroy any salmon spawn or spawning bed, or to impede salmon in their passage to such a bed during the annual close time. The exceptions in (b) above apply also in this case.

(d)   Unclean Salmon

The taking or attempted taking of kelts or unclean or unseasonable fish is an offence under Section 20 of the 1868 Act. There are exemptions if the kelt or unseasonable fish is accidentally taken and returned to the water immediately, or if it is used for artificial propagation or scientific purposes.

(e)   Dead Salmon

It is an offence under Section 6 of the *Salmon and Freshwater Fisheries (Protection) (Scotland) Act 1951* to remove a dead salmon from any waters including the sea up to one mile from low water mark unless the person so doing is duly authorised to do so.

FURTHER READING

Mills, D H   1965   *The Distribution and Food of the Cormorant in Scottish Inland Waters* (HMSO)

Mills, D H	1962	*The Goosander and Red Breasted Merganser as Predators of Salmon in Scottish Waters* (HMSO)
Sinha, V R P and Jones, J W	1967	On the Food of the Freshwater Eels and their Feeding Relationships with the Salmonids (*J. Zool, Lond. 153, 119-137*)

24 Seals

(a) Distribution

The two species of seal which inhabit the seas around Britain are the common and the grey. The common seal is the smaller animal very widely distributed around the world, but not so numerous in Britain as the grey seal. Grey seals on the other hand are rare on the world count, but have several important breeding colonies around Scotland so that about two thirds of the world population is based on Scotland. In addition the largest of the English breeding colonies on the Farne Islands is close to the Scottish border. The main breeding colonies in Scotland are on the Orkneys, Shetlands, North Rona and Hebrides.

(b) Population

The Grey Seals Protection Act 1914 was the first Act to protect grey seals in Britain, when the species was thought to be in danger of extinction. The population at that time was estimated by H Hesketh Prichard and the promoters of the Act to be as low as 500 individuals. In 1927 it was estimated that the Scottish population had increased to over 5,000. In 1963 the Report of the Consultative Committee on

Grey Seals and Fisheries reckoned that the population based on the Scottish breeding colonies had reached 30,000 and by 1974 this figure was estimated to be 45,000. At the same time the population based on the Farne Islands had increased from about 100 individuals in 1920 to an estimated 5,800 in 1974.

(c) Breeding

Common seals breed on sandbanks in the summer and the pups can swim a few hours after they are born. Grey seals which roam the North Atlantic for the rest of the year, return to their breeding colony of origin in October or November for just a few weeks. During this period they give birth and conceive the following year's pup after a short interval. It is about three weeks before the pups are able to swim. This means that effective culling of grey seal populations can only take place during the breeding season.

(d) Food of Grey Seals

Grey seals are almost exclusively fish eaters. Stomach content analyses have shown that a number of commercially important fish species, including salmonids, figure prominently in the diet. The percentage of salmonids in the diet has been found to vary from as little as 4% in Shetland to almost 30% on the Scottish East Coast. It has been estimated by Dr B B Rae that the average daily consumption of fish by each adult grey seal is 15 lbs. (See Further Reading).

(e) Damage Caused by Seals

Grey seals kill and maim considerable numbers of salmon in Scottish waters and this situation is aggravated by the population explosion among these seals. Common seals are less destructive but where they are present in large numbers they cause considerable damage. Seals also cause damage to fishing gear while in pursuit of salmon.

(f) Conservation

Conservation is controlled at present by the *Conservation of Seals Act 1970*. This creates an Annual

Close Season for grey seals from 1st September to 31st December, and for common seals from 1st June to 31st August. At other times of the year it is lawful to kill seals, although it is an offence to use either poison, or a rifle with ammunition having a muzzle velocity of less than 600 footpounds or a bullet weighing less than 45 grains. However, during the close season licences can also be obtained by fishermen from the Secretary of State for the purpose of the prevention of damage to fisheries.

(g) Culling

In view of the population increases and the damage caused by seals, a pup culling programme has been undertaken in recent years in Scotland. This is implemented through the issue of licences to seal hunters by the Secretary of State for Scotland to kill seals during the close season, the size of the culls being based on advice from the Natural Environment Research Council.

FURTHER READING

Report of the Consultative Committee on Grey Seals & Fisheries 1963 (HMSO)

Rae, B B	1960	*Seals & Scottish Fisheries* (HMSO)
Rae, B B and Shearer, W M	1965	*Seal Damage to Salmon Fisheries* (HMSO)
Rae, B B	1968	*The Food of Seals in Scottish Waters* (HMSO)
Bonner, W N	1976	*Stocks of Grey Seals and Common Seals in Great Britain* (NERC)

25 Land Drainage

(a) Development

In Scotland during the post war period, large acreages of land have been improved or reclaimed for agricultural purposes or developed for forestry. Much of this land is situated in the headwaters of our river systems. These developments have brought with them drainage systems which may extend over quite large areas.

(b) Agriculture

Improvement of hill pasture has involved the provision of long lengths of open drains which follow the contours of the land into hill burns or main leaders. The leaders normally consist of open ditches with sloping sides which in turn lead into the river systems.

(c) Forestry

Forestry land is normally ploughed before planting, with each furrow becoming a potential drain on steep slopes. These areas are drained with small open drains leading into a burn or main leader.

(d) Water Flow

The change from seeping drainage to man-made drainage tends to alter the normal regime of many of our rivers. Rivers that rose and fell slowly from a catchment which held water for a considerable period after rainfall, now often rise and fall more quickly.

(e) Effect on Fisheries

Improvements in land drainage can often result in higher water velocities, which may in turn cause erosion of the banks and beds of water courses. The movement of gravel and silt during periods of high water velocity poses problems for fishery management, as the destruction of redds and bottom fauna can occur. Further, the long periods of water scarcity, which can follow rapid drainage, create problems particularly in nursery areas. In effect the environment of a river system can be changed by land drainage developments.

26 Obstructions

(a)   Powers of District Boards

It is illegal both at Common Law and by Statute to place any obstruction in a river so as to impede the passage of salmon or sea trout. Schedule G of the *Salmon Fisheries (Scotland) Act 1868* sets out the regulations regarding dams and other artificial obstructions and the measures to be taken to ensure that the least possible amount of harm is done to salmon fisheries. The Schedule was applied to the Tweed by the *Salmon & Freshwater Fisheries (Protection) (Scotland) Act 1951.*

The position with regard to natural obstructions is that they can be removed, or fish passes provided to assist fish to overcome them, by either District Boards or proprietors. District Boards must first reach agreement with the proprietors affected before the Board can remove obstructions, or make them passable.

A proprietor is free to alter a natural obstruction on his own property, providing he does not interfere with the rights of others.

(b)   Fishing at Falls and in Fish Passes

Section 15(5) of the 1868 Act makes it an offence to use

any net or other engine for taking salmon jumping at falls or falling back after trying to jump at falls.

Section 15(6) of the same Act makes it an offence to take salmon in any fish pass, or to impede their passage through a fish pass.

27 Hydro-Electric Development

The introduction of hydro-electric schemes on a number of rivers suitable for that type of development created serious problems so far as salmon were concerned inasmuch as interference with natural flows affected spawning facilities, feeding grounds and fishings. The dams and other constructions, with their associated installations, presented obstacles to descending smolts and kelts and ascending adult fish. The hydro-electric schemes were exempted from the terms of Schedule G of the *Salmon Fisheries (Scotland) Act 1868* which regulated the construction and use of mill dams, lades and water wheels. Special provisions were included, however, in the various schemes for the purpose of avoiding as far as possible damage to fisheries and the stock of salmon. These provisions included fish passes, fish lifts, smolt screens, compensation water, easement of obstacles, and in some cases hatcheries. In some instances, financial compensation was paid for damage to fisheries.

The *Hydro-Electric Development (Scotland) Act 1943* which established the North of Scotland Hydro-Electric Board also provided for an independent Fisheries Committee to advise on proposed schemes and their later operation. In 1955, Section 9 of the above Act was extended to cover the South of Scotland Electricity Board area.

The dams of the North of Scotland Hydro-Electric Board provide excellent sites for fish counting. Statistics provided by that Board and by the South of Scotland Electricity Board are set out in Appendix III.

28 Associations

There are a number of bodies concerned with the conservation of the salmon species and the proper regulation of the different legal methods of fishing.

The *Association of Scottish District Salmon Fishery Boards* is representative of the different Fishery Boards and deals with matters of common interest to these Boards. It is recognised as an authority in a position to submit to the Government of the day informed opinion and balanced judgement on any legislative changes under consideration.

The *Salmon Net Fishing Association of Scotland* represents the commercial salmon operators and is the official channel of communication between the industry and the appropriate government departments.

The *Scottish Salmon Anglers' Federation* represents salmon anglers on a national basis and is in a position to express collective views of salmon rod fishermen.

Among other bodies are the *Scottish Committee of the Salmon and Trout Association* which has both net and rod members and concerns itself with the more general aspects of salmon fishing, the *Scottish Committee of the Anglers' Co-operative Association* which is primarily concerned with measures to prevent or eliminate pollution and the *Scottish Landowners' Federation* which is supported by riparian owners and has salmon fishing only as one of its interests.

Secretaries

ASDSFB   Norman A Cockburn, WS, 19 Ainslie Place, Edinburgh EH3 6AY

SNFAS   Allan McKendrick, Solicitor, 9 Bon-Accord Crescent, Aberdeen AB1 2DN

SSAF	W & J Burness, WS, 12 Hope Street, Edinburgh
S & T A	J R Gardiner, WS, 7 Rothesay Terrace, Edinburgh EH3 7SD
ACA	Duncan J McGregor, 10 Corrennie Drive, Edinburgh EH10 6EQ
SLF	A F Roney-Dougal, 18 Abercromby Place, Edinburgh EH3 6TY

29 Statistics

The *Salmon and Freshwater Fisheries (Protection) (Scotland) Act 1951* empowers the Secretary of State to collect statistics relating to the number of migratory fish caught in any salmon fishery. The statistics are to be furnished in such form and at such times as the Secretary of State may order, and he has power to publish them in an appropriate manner to show the catch in any district by rod and line, by nets within estuarial limits, and by nets outside the limits. However, the published statistics must not disclose the actual numbers of salmon caught in any one fishery within the period of ten years preceding such publication.

The Department of Agriculture and Fisheries for Scotland receives annually returns of monthly catches of salmon, grilse and sea-trout from all rod and net proprietors, and publishes annually the total Scottish catches, taken separately by rods, net and coble and fixed engines. In addition the Freshwater Fisheries Laboratory examines the returns of catches by District, to assess trends over the years. Catch records are available since 1952, and Appendix IV gives the catches of salmon taken annually since 1952, in four areas covering the whole of Scotland.

30 Glossary

assessment
— fishery rates paid by owners of fishings to District Salmon Fishery Boards.

close times
— periods during which the catching of fish is forbidden.

coble
— a flat bottomed boat used for salmon fishing in Scotland.

cruive
— an almost obsolete trap for catching salmon in rivers. A cruive may consist of a low dam built across a river with one or more traps built into it; alternatively the trap may be built into a natural waterfall or obstruction.

drift net
— a net suspended down from the surface of the sea by means of floats and a weighted bottom rope. It is allowed to drift with the tide and is made of a twine so fine that fish do not see it and because of its mesh size become entangled in it.

estuary limits	— the line which divides a river from the sea. For legal purposes in Scotland these are defined for each river under Schedule B of the *Salmon Fisheries (Scotland) Act 1868.*
engine	— an ancient word for a means of taking salmon.
eyed ova	— eggs of salmon about three months after spawning, when the eyes of the developing fish can be seen through the shell.
fish pass (or ladder)	— a structure designed to help migratory fish surmount or descend an obstruction in a river.
fixed engine	— a salmon trap which is fixed in one place. (See Chapter 10).
foul hooking	— hooking a fish other than in the mouth.
fry	— see Chapter 1.
gaff	— a large sharply pointed hook attached to the end of a long handle and used for taking salmon from the water.
grilse	— see Chapter 1.
hang net	— an anchored net made of a twine so fine that fish do not see it and because of its mesh size become entangled in it.

heck	— a grating placed at the foot of a water course as a barrier to stop the ascent of migratory fish.
interdict	— a civil process of law whereby a person asks the courts to stop another person interfering with his rights.
kelt	— see Chapter 1.
lade	— the channel of water diverted from a main stream by a dam and usually associated with a mill.
leister	— an instrument with barbed prongs used for spearing salmon.
long line	— a floating line sometimes miles in length with baited hooks attached at intervals and used for catching fish on their marine feeding grounds.
medium filum	— an imaginary line drawn down the centre of a river. (See Chapter 3).
net and coble	— the method of fishing for salmon by using a sweep net worked from a boat. (See Chapter 10).
otter	— when used for taking salmon illegally, a floating board so constructed that it runs out a line, to which baits and lures are attached.

ova	— see Chapter 1.
parr	— see Chapter 1.
prescriptive period	— the interval after which possession of a heritable right for a period of years operates to cure defects in the original title.
Procurator Fiscal	— the Crown Prosecutor.
redd	— the excavation of gravel on the stream bed into which salmon deposit their eggs.
smolt	— see Chapter 1.
sniggering and snatching	— a form of rod and line fishing in which fish are deliberately foul hooked.
tacksman	— the lessee of a salmon net fishery.
unclean fish	— a salmon which has recently spawned and which has not recovered its condition by resuming its sea feeding.

Appendix I

West Greenland Salmon Catches

(metric tonnes)

Year	Offshore Drift Net	Onshore Gill Net and Drift Net b	Total
1960	–	60	60
1961	–	127	127
1962	–	244	244
1963	–	466	466
1964	–	1539	1539
1965	36+	825	861+
1966	119	1251	1370
1967	318	1283	1601
1968	548	579	1127
1969	850	1360b	2210
1970	895	1244	2146c
1971	1240	1449	2689
1972	720	1320	2040
1973	771	1585	2356
1974	755	1199	1954
1975a	858	1194	2052

a Provisional data.

b Up to 1968 gill-net only; after 1968 gill-net and drift net.

c Including 7 tonnes caught by long line by one of two Greenland vessels in the Labrador Sea – early 1970.

Appendix II

Scottish Salmon Fishery Districts, Rateable Values and Close Times

DISTRICTS WITH FISHERY BOARDS

	Rateable Value (1975) £	Annual Close Time for Net Fishing	Annual Close Time for Rod Fishing
Add	159	Sep 1 – Feb 15	Nov 1 – Feb 15
Alness	2220	Aug 27 – Feb 10	Nov 1 – Feb 10
Annan	9034	Sep 10 – Feb 24	Nov 16 – Feb 24
Awe	3875	Aug 27 – Feb 10	Oct 16 – Feb 10
Ayr	840	Aug 27 – Feb 10	Nov 1 – Feb 10
Bervie	1087	Sep 10 – Feb 24	Nov 1 – Feb 24
Broom	435	Aug 27 – Feb 10	Nov 1 – Feb 10
Brora	2100	Aug 27 – Feb 10	Oct 16 – Jan 31
Clayburn (Harris)	107	Sep 10 – Feb 24	Nov 1 – Feb 24
Conon	8109	Aug 27 – Feb 10	Oct 1 – Jan 25
Cree	2997	Sep 14 – Feb 28	Oct 1 – Feb 28
Creed (Lewis)	1600	Aug 27 – Feb 10	Oct 17 – Feb 10
Dee (Aberdeenshire)	51552	Aug 27 – Feb 10	Oct 1 – Jan 31
Dee (Kirkcudbright)	537	Aug 27 – Feb 10	Nov 1 – Feb 10
Deveron	13936	Aug 27 – Feb 10	Nov 1 – Feb 10
Don	16058	Aug 27 – Feb 10	Nov 1 – Feb 10
Doon	1346	Aug 27 – Feb 10	Nov 1 – Feb 10
Dunbeath	223	Aug 27 – Feb 10	Oct 16 – Feb 10
North Esk	22180	Sep 1 – Feb 15	Nov 1 – Feb 15
South Esk	14577	Sep 1 – Feb 15	Nov 1 – Feb 15
Ewe	1740	Aug 27 – Feb 10	Nov 1 – Feb 10
Fincastle (Harris)	430	Sep 10 – Feb 24	Nov 1 – Feb 24
Findhorn	6164	Aug 27 – Feb 10	Oct 1 – Feb 10

	Rate-able Value (1975) £	Annual Close Time for Net Fishing	Annual Close Time for Rod Fishing
Forss	431	Aug 27 – Feb 10	Nov 1 – Feb 10
Forth	1718	Aug 27 – Feb 10	Nov 1 – Jan 31
Girvan	904	Sep 10 – Feb 24	Nov 1 – Feb 24
Gruinard and Little Gruinard	1650	Aug 27 – Feb 10	Nov 1 – Feb 10
Halladale	1205	Aug 27 – Feb 10	Oct 1 – Jan 11
Helmsdale	2820	Aug 27 – Feb 10	Oct 1 – Jan 10
Hope and Polla	684	Aug 27 – Feb 10	Oct 1 – Jan 11
Kinloch (Kyle of Tongue)	65	Aug 27 – Feb 10	Nov 1 – Feb 10
Kyle of Sutherland	9620	Aug 27 – Feb 10	Oct 1 – Jan 10
Lochy	2420	Aug 27 – Feb 10	Nov 1 – Feb 10
Loch Roag (Lewis)	2530	Aug 27 – Feb 10	Oct 17 – Feb 10
Luce	748	Sep 10 – Feb 24	Nov 1 – Feb 24
Nairn	1140	Aug 27 – Feb 10	Oct 1 – Feb 10
Naver and Borgie	2100	Aug 27 – Feb 10	Oct 1 – Jan 11
Ness	4459	Aug 27 – Feb 10	Oct 16 – Jan 14
Nith	4220	Sep 10 – Feb 24	Dec 1 – Feb 24
Spey	44120	Aug 27 – Feb 10	Oct 1 – Feb 10
Stinchar	1284	Sep 10 – Feb 24	Nov 1 – Feb 24
Tay }	75811	Aug 21 – Feb 4	Oct 16 – Jan 14
Earn }			Nov 1 – Jan 31
Thurso	2637	Aug 27 – Feb 10	Oct 6 – Jan 10
Ugie	1793	Sep 10 – Feb 24	Nov 1 – Feb 9
Ullapool	80	Aug 27 – Feb 10	Nov 1 – Feb 10
Wick	276	Aug 27 – Feb 10	Nov 1 – Feb 10
Ythan	3126	Sep 10 – Feb 24	Nov 1 – Feb 10

DISTRICTS IN WHICH NO BOARDS HAVE BEEN CONSTITUTED

Ailort	Aug 27 – Feb 10	Nov 1 – Feb 10
Aline	Aug 27 – Feb 10	Nov 1 – Feb 10
Applecross	Aug 27 – Feb 10	Nov 1 – Feb 10
Arnisdale (Loch Hourn)	Aug 27 – Feb 10	Nov 1 – Feb 10
Baa and Goladoir (Mull)	Aug 27 – Feb 10	Nov 1 – Feb 10

	Annual Close Time for Net Fishing	Annual Close Time for Rod Fishing
Badachro and Kerry (Gairloch)	Aug 27 – Feb 10	Nov 1 – Feb 10
Beauly	Aug 27 – Feb 10	Oct 16 – Feb 10
Berriedale	Aug 27 – Feb 10	Nov 1 – Feb 10
Bladenoch	Aug 27 – Feb 10	Nov 1 – Feb 10
Carradale (Kintyre)	Sep 10 – Feb 24	Nov 1 – Feb 24
Carron (W. Ross)	Aug 27 – Feb 10	Nov 1 – Feb 10
Clyde and Leven	Aug 27 – Feb 10	Nov 1 – Feb 10
Creran	Aug 27 – Feb 10	Nov 1 – Feb 10
Croe and Shiel (Loch Duich)	Aug 27 – Feb 10	Nov 1 – Feb 10
Drummachloy or Glenmore (Bute)	Sep 1 – Feb 15	Oct 16 – Feb 15
Eackaig	Sep 1 – Feb 15	Nov 1 – Feb 15
Fleet (Sutherland)	Sep 10 – Feb 24	Nov 1 – Feb 24
Fleet (Kirkcudbright)	Sep 10 – Feb 24	Nov 1 – Feb 24
Fyne, Shira and Aray	Sep 1 – Feb 15	Nov 1 – Feb 15
Glenelg	Aug 27 – Feb 10	Nov 1 – Feb 10
Gour	Aug 27 – Feb 10	Nov 1 – Feb 10
Greiss, Laxdale and Tong or Thunga (Lewis)	Aug 27 – Feb 10	Nov 1 – Feb 10
Grudie or Dionard	Aug 27 – Feb 10	Nov 1 – Feb 10
Howmore (whole of South Uist, Benbecula and Barra)	Sep 10 – Feb 24	Nov 1 – Feb 24
Inchard	Aug 27 – Feb 10	Nov 1 – Feb 10
Inner (whole of Jura)	Sep 10 – Feb 24	Nov 1 – Feb 24
Inver	Aug 27 – Feb 10	Nov 1 – Feb 10
Iorsa (whole of Arran)	Sep 10 – Feb 24	Nov 1 – Feb 24
Irvine and Garnock	Sep 10 – Feb 24	Nov 1 – Feb 24
Kannaird	Aug 27 – Feb 10	Nov 1 – Feb 10
Kilchoan or Inverie (Loch Nevis)	Aug 27 – Feb 10	Nov 1 – Feb 10
Kirkaig	Aug 27 – Feb 10	Nov 1 – Feb 10
Kishorn	Aug 27 – Feb 10	Nov 1 – Feb 10
Laggan and Sorn (whole of Islay)	Sep 10 – Feb 24	Nov 1 – Feb 24
Laxford	Aug 27 – Feb 10	Nov 1 – Feb 10
Little Loch Broom	Aug 27 – Feb 10	Nov 1 – Feb 10

68

	Annual Close Time for Net Fishing	*Annual Close Time for Rod Fishing*
Leven (Kinlochleven)	Aug 27 – Feb 10	Nov 1 – Feb 10
Loch Long (Ling and Elchaig)	Aug 27 – Feb 10	Nov 1 – Feb 10
Lossie	Aug 27 – Feb 10	Oct 16 – Feb 10
Lussa (Mull)	Aug 27 – Feb 10	Nov 1 – Feb 10
Moidart	Aug 27 – Feb 10	Nov 1 – Feb 10
Morar	Aug 27 – Feb 10	Nov 1 – Feb 10
Mullanageren, Horasary and Lochnaciste (whole of North Uist)	Sep 10 – Feb 24	Nov 1 – Feb 24
Nell, Feochan and Euchar	Aug 27 – Feb 10	Nov 1 – Feb 10
Orkney Islands (River from Loch of Stenness, etc.)	Sep 10 – Feb 24	Nov 1 – Feb 24
Ormsary, Loch Head and Stornoway (Kintyre)	Aug 27 – Feb 10	Nov 1 – Feb 10
Pennygowan or Glenforsa and Aros (Mull)	Aug 27 – Feb 10	Nov 1 – Feb 10
Resort (Lewis)	Aug 27 – Feb 10	Nov 1 – Feb 10
Ruel (Kyles of Bute)	Sep 1 – Feb 15	Nov 1 – Feb 15
Sanda	Aug 27 – Feb 10	Nov 1 – Feb 10
Scaddle	Aug 27 – Feb 10	Nov 1 – Feb 10
Shetland Islands (River of Sandwater, etc.)	Sep 10 – Feb 24	Nov 1 – Feb 24
Shiel (Loch Shiel)	Aug 27 – Feb 10	Nov 1 – Feb 10
Sligachan, Broadford and Portree (Skye)	Aug 27 – Feb 10	Nov 1 – Feb 10
Snizort, Otley, Oze and Drynoch (Skye)	Aug 27 – Feb 10	Nov 1 – Feb 10
Strathy	Aug 27 – Feb 10	Oct 1 – Jan 11
Sunart (Loch)	Aug 27 – Feb 10	Nov 1 – Feb 10
Torridon, Balgay and Shieldaig	Aug 27 – Feb 10	Nov 1 – Feb 10
Urr	Sep 10 – Feb 24	Nov 30 – Feb 24
Special Area		
Tweed (administered by Tweed Commissioners)	Sep 15 – Feb 14	Dec 1 – Jan 31

Note: In many cases modern spelling has been adopted.

Appendix

River System	Fish Pass Location	1965	1966	1967	1968
Shin	Diversion Dam	239	213	226	191
	Lairg	199	138	89	—
Conon	Torr Achilty	2883	2436	4933	2404
	Meig	829	546	835	160
	Luichart	526	232	552	307
Beauly	Kilmorack	8900	8670	13956	4903
	Aigas	8641	8390	12749	4300
	Beannachran	203	146	264	124
Ness	Invergarry	377	371	320	166
	Dundreggan	349	347	346	222
Spey	Tromie	470	386	401	223
Tay	Pitlochry	4558	4879	6148	4365
	Clunie	168	77	96	86
	Stronuich	154	162	185	153
	Falls of Lochay	277	113	276	217
Lochy	Mucomir	959	576	553	286
Awe	Inverawe	3831	3117	4471	3619

SOUTH OF SCOTLAND

Dee (Kirkcudbright)	Tongland	6536	4789	10136	5574

† From 14th June, 1974.
‡ To 30th September only.

II

rilse at Fish Passes

YDRO-ELECTRIC BOARD

969	1970	1971	1972	1973	1974	1975
195	148*	265	150	76	76	116
–	–	–	62	6	16	21
486	2277	5173	6224	3496	3395	1362
266	294	572	345	240	585	49
402	224	413	298¶	96	296	120
248	5194	19621	5356	7890	7842	5601
983	4769	8954	5315	7362	7150	5393
200	92	250	470	124	339	213
226	192	269	230	280	258	564
219	262	321	403	521	485	572
427	418	485	571	230	16†	38
361	5253	6186	7771	11977	8250	6710
77	52	77	151	194	141	224
43*	103	254	356	340	362	138
168	312	475	145	351	231	115
676	550	615	652	601	444	455
719	2942	4488	3631	3700	3528	2579

LECTRICITY BOARD

407	1222	1793	1393	828	997‡	397

Counter working only for part season.
Trap removed on 26th September, 1972, because of poachers.

Appendix

Numbers of Salmon and Grilse Caught

Year	East Coast (Tweed – Ugie)		Moray Firth and North Coast (Deveron – Naver)	
	Salmon	Grilse	Salmon	Grilse
1952	147069	66470	65427	66999
1953	127456	61933	60814	55906
1954	157580	51056	72643	42884
1955	139752	46864	82898	65831
1956	114612	47059	60094	48820
1957	126143	74151	59066	77531
1958	121645	81164	67026	67018
1959	182943	54539	56594	39227
1960	119297	82083	55341	64128
1961	107143	76759	48411	55077
1962	118170	147764	57602	74238
1963	168108	73298	62865	47167
1964	151655	134471	74866	88933
1965	126507	97720	57916	66278
1966	140176	109525	52171	64051
1967	149502	166126	68984	111548
1968	130668	100250	50416	57722
1969	136091	209918	46102	92780
1970	112683	157273	35158	53972
1971	96160	140188	38382	77184
1972	117749	142126	58480	78112
1973	140266	180977	58179	79997
1974	101301	141220	56894	98575
1975	109833	110772	68195	62786

East Coast – Bervie, Dee, Don, North Esk, South Esk, Forth, Tay, Tweed, Ugie, Ythan.

Moray Firth and North Coast – Alness, Beauly, Berriedale, Brora, Conon, Deveron, Dunbeath, Findhorn, Fleet, Forss, Halladale, Helmsdale, Kyle of Sutherland, Lossie, Nairn, Naver and Borgie, Ness, Spey, Strathy, Thurso, Wick, Shetland.

West Coast – Add, Aline, Applecross, Arnisdale, Awe, Ailort, Baa, Badachro, Broom, Carradale, Carron, Clayburn, Creed, Creran, Croe and Shiel, Ewe, Fincastle, Loch Fyne, Glenelg, Greiss, Grudie,

IV

by Nets and Rods in Scotland, 1952-1975

West Coast (Hope – Loch Fyne)		South West Coast (Ruel – Annan)		Total Catch	
Salmon	Grilse	Salmon	Grilse	Salmon	Grilse
10625	11204	12203	5552	235324	150225
11946	17080	11979	7201	212195	142120
12523	16343	13512	6783	256258	117066
12500	14558	15364	8846	250514	136099
10846	11892	11826	8927	197378	116698
15994	29130	16242	15963	217445	196775
15854	29234	18235	19352	222760	196768
9549	10025	20890	11159	269976	114950
8944	19664	16758	17534	200340	183409
8687	13744	15594	10667	179835	156247
15870	29124	21142	30170	212784	281296
13323	25715	22844	20699	267140	166879
19873	33975	22389	28158	268783	285537
15822	26061	19692	241132	219937	214191
12345	22216	23012	25090	227704	220882
19393	30794	23612	36461	261491	344929
15890	29838	16957	26060	213931	213870
12904	22430	14855	23649	209952	348777
14518	16062	11938	16130	174297	243437
16446	30784	10081	14551	161069	262707
25117	19300	9038	10178	210384	249736
20841	19577	10102	10889	229388	291440
15577	21249	11699	17379	185471	278423
19094	24303	12616	16390	209738	214251

Kannaird, Kilchoan, Kinloch, Kirkaig, Kishorn, Laggan and Sorn, Laxford, Leven, Little Loch Broom, Lochy, Loch Long, Loch Roag, Lussa, Moidart, Morar, Mullanageren, Nell, Ormsary, Pennygowan, Sanda, Scaddle, Shiel, Sligachan, Snizort, Sunart, Torridon, Ullapool.
South West Coast – Annan, Ayr, Bladenoch, Clyde, Cree, Dee, Doon, Drummachloy, Eachaig, Fleet, Girvan, Irvine, Luce, Nith, Ruel, Stinchar, Urr.
N.B. This table includes corrections to figures which have been published in earlier reports.

Appendix

Value of Catch, Assessable Value, District Fishery

Year	Estimated Value of Total Salmon Catch by all Methods £	Total Assessable Value of Salmon Fisheries in Districts for which Boards exist, including the Tweed £
1960	1243369	212284
1961	1181663	202695
1962	1463455	223502
1963	1367865	228789
1964	1479217	232489
1965	1619593	228303
1966	1780000	252347
1967	2052700	277323
1968	1788500	299668
1969	2354000	299531
1970	1610000	299497
1971	1823834	308978
1972	3079739	350009
1973	3062733	352066
1974	2742982	347742
1975	3377730	352544

V

Board Assessment Raised and Netsmen Employed

Year	Fishery Board Assessment Raised in Districts for which Boards exist, including the Tweed £	Number of Men Directly Employed in Salmon Net Fishing in Scotland
1960	51537	1644
1961	56588	1630
1962	64110	1663
1963	66548	1613
1964	69055	1583
1965	72817	1600
1966	79543	1543
1967	94675	1514
1968	92057	1568
1969	96883	1485
1970	100620	1418
1971	106204	1390
1972	114416	1304
1973	126829	1161
1974	140744	1221
1975	170191	1247

Appendix VI.

River Purification Boards
in Scotland

Clyde River Purification Board,
Rivers House, Murray Road,
East Kilbride,
Glasgow G75 0LA.   *Tel. No.* East Kilbride 38181

Forth River Purification Board,
Colinton Dell House,
West Mills Road, Colinton,
Edinburgh EH13 0NX.   *Tel. No.* 031-441 4691

Highland River Purification Board,
Town House,
Dingwall.   *Tel. No.* Dingwall 2267

North East River Purification Board,
Woodside House,
Persley,
Aberdeen AB2 2UQ.   *Tel. No.* Aberdeen 492647

Solway River Purification Board,
39 Castle Street,
Dumfries DG1 1DL.   *Tel. No.* Dumfries 63031

Tay River Purification Board,
3 South Street,
Perth PH2 8NJ.   *Tel. No.* Perth 27980

Tweed River Purification Board,
Burnbrae, Mossilee Road,
Galashiels,
Selkirkshire TD1 1NF.   *Tel. No.* Galashiels 2425

List of other books published by Fishing News Books Limited

1 Long Garden Walk, Farnham, Surrey, England

Free catalogue available on request

A living from lobsters
Aquaculture practices in Taiwan
Better angling with simple science
British freshwater fishes
Coastal aquaculture in the Indo-Pacific region
Commercial fishing methods
Control of fish quality
Culture of bivalve molluscs
Eel capture, culture, processing and marketing
Eel culture
European inland water fish: a multilingual catalogue
FAO catalogue of fishing gear designs
FAO catalogue of small scale fishing gear
FAO investigates ferro-cement fishing craft
Farming the edge of the sea
Fish and shellfish farming in coastal waters
Fish catching methods of the world
Fish farming international No 2
Fish inspection and quality control
Fisheries oceanography
Fishery products
Fishing boats of the world 1

Fishing boats of the world 2
Fishing boats of the world 3
Fishing ports and markets
Fishing with electricity
Fishing with light
Freezing and irradiation of fish
Handbook of trout and salmon diseases
Handy medical guide for seafarers
How to make and set nets
Inshore fishing: its skills, risks, rewards
International regulation of marine fisheries: a study of
  regional fisheries organizations
Marine pollution and sea life
Mechanization of small fishing craft
Mending of fishing nets
Modern deep sea trawling gear
Modern fishing gear of the world 1
Modern fishing gear of the world 2
Modern fishing gear of the world 3
Modern inshore fishing gear
More Scottish fishing craft and their work
Multilingual dictionary of fish and fish products
Navigation primer for fishermen
Netting materials for fishing gear
Pair trawling and pair seining—the technology of two boat
  fishing
Pelagic and semi-pelagic trawling gear
Planning aquaculture development—an introductory guide
Power transmission and automation for ships and
  submersibles
Refrigeration on fishing vessels
Seafood fishing for amateur and professional
Ships' gear 66
Sonar in fisheries: a forward look
Stability and trim of fishing vessels
Testing the freshness of frozen fish
Textbook of fish culture; breeding and cultivation of fish
The fertile sea

The fish resources of the ocean
The fishing cadet's handbook
The lemon sole
The marketing of shellfish
The seine net: its origin, evolution and use
The stern trawler
The stocks of whales
Trawlermen's handbook
Tuna: distribution and migration
Underwater observation using sonar